KURTIS J. WIEBE & TYLER JENKINS

Shadowline™

image

www.ShadowlineOnline.com

PETER PANZERFAUST VOLUME ONE: THE GREAT ESCAPE

Third Printing , DECEMBER 2013   ISBN: 978-1-60706-854-9

Published by Image Comics, Inc. Office of publication: 2001 Center Street, Sixth Floor, Berkeley,
California 94704. Copyright © 2014 KURTIS J. WIEBE and TYLER JENKINS. Originally published
in single magazine form as PETER PANZERFAUST #1-5. All rights reserved. PETER
PANZERFAUST™ (including all prominent characters featured herein), its logo and all character
likenesses are trademarks of KURTIS J. WIEBE and TYLER JENKINS, unless otherwise noted.
Image Comics® and its logos are registered trademarks of Image Comics, Inc. Shadowline and its
logos are ™ and © 2014 Jim Valentino. No part of this publication may be reproduced or transmitted
in any form or by any means (except for short excerpts for review purposes) without the express
written permission of Mr. Wiebe and/or Jenkins. All names, characters, events and locales in this
publication are entirely fictional. Any resemblance to actual persons (living or dead), events or
places, without satiric intent, is coincidental. For information regarding the CPSIA on this printed
material call: 203-595-3636 and provide reference # RICH – 537750. PRINTED IN USA.
International Rights / Foreign Licensing -- foreignlicensing@imagecomics.com

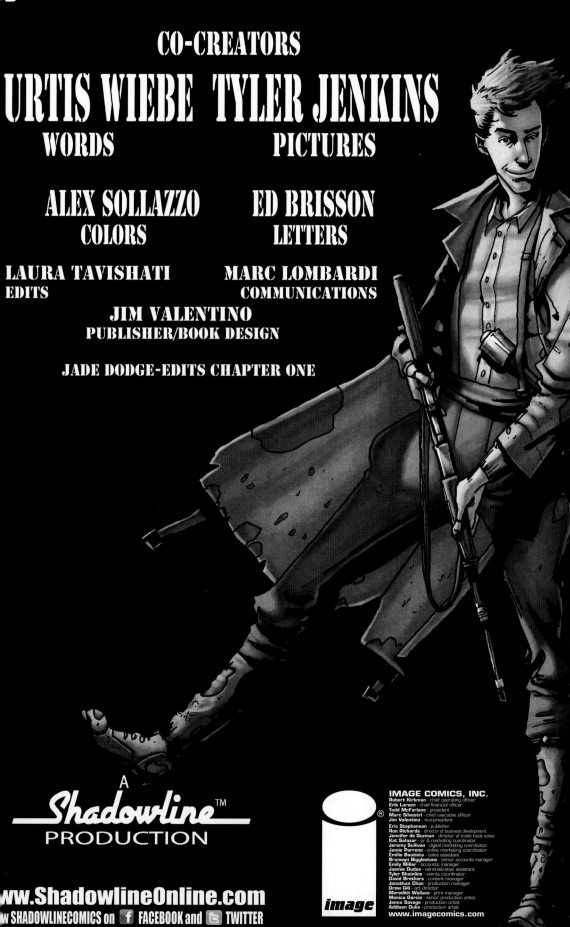

ge COMICS PRESENTS

CO-CREATORS

URTIS WIEBE TYLER JENKINS
WORDS
PICTURES

ALEX SOLLAZZO
COLORS

ED BRISSON
LETTERS

LAURA TAVISHATI
EDITS

MARC LOMBARDI
COMMUNICATIONS

JIM VALENTINO
PUBLISHER/BOOK DESIGN

JADE DODGE-EDITS CHAPTER ONE

A
Shadowline™
PRODUCTION

IMAGE COMICS, INC.
Robert Kirkman - chief operating officer
Erik Larsen - chief financial officer
Todd McFarlane - president
Marc Silvestri - chief executive officer
Jim Valentino - vice-president

Eric Stephenson - publisher
Ron Richards - director of business development
Jennifer de Guzman - director of trade book sales
Kat Salazar - pr & marketing coordinator
Jeremy Sullivan - digital marketing coordinator
Jamie Parreno - online marketing coordinator
Emilio Bautista - sales assistant
Branwyn Bigglestone - senior accounts manager
Emily Miller - accounts manager
Jaemie Dudas - administrative assistant
Tyler Shainline - events coordinator
David Brothers - content manager
Jonathan Chan - production manager
Drew Gill - art director
Meredith Wallace - print manager
Monica Garcia - senior production artist
Jenna Savage - production artist
Addison Duke - production artist
www.imagecomics.com

ww.ShadowlineOnline.com

w SHADOWLINECOMICS on f FACEBOOK and t TWITTER

image

"To the memory of J.M. Barrie
for creating a magical world that the child in all of us can explore."

Kurtis J. Wiebe

"To my wife, Hilary.
    To my Family.
        To grand adventure and wild heroics."

Tyler Jenkins

CHAPTER ONE

ISSUE ONE COVER B

THIS IS WHERE YOU MET THE BOYS?

OUI, THE LOT OF US, EACH AS LOST AS THE NEXT. NO PARENTS, NO MONEY, NO FUTURE. BUT, WE HAD EACH OTHER, AS HOKEY AS IT SOUNDS.

DID THE BOYS GIVE YOU THE NICKNAME TOOTLES?

NO, THAT CAME LATER.

WITH PETER?

YES, WITH PETER.

WHAT IS YOUR FIRST MEMORY OF HIM?

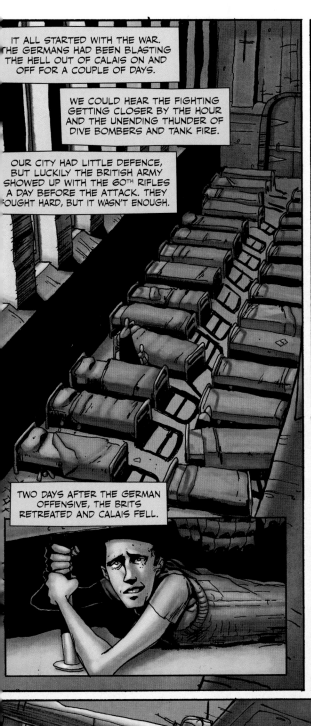

IT ALL STARTED WITH THE WAR. THE GERMANS HAD BEEN BLASTING THE HELL OUT OF CALAIS ON AND OFF FOR A COUPLE OF DAYS.

WE COULD HEAR THE FIGHTING GETTING CLOSER BY THE HOUR AND THE UNENDING THUNDER OF DIVE BOMBERS AND TANK FIRE.

OUR CITY HAD LITTLE DEFENCE, BUT LUCKILY THE BRITISH ARMY SHOWED UP WITH THE 60TH RIFLES A DAY BEFORE THE ATTACK. THEY FOUGHT HARD, BUT IT WASN'T ENOUGH.

TWO DAYS AFTER THE GERMAN OFFENSIVE, THE BRITS RETREATED AND CALAIS FELL.

OF COURSE, YOU WEREN'T ASKING ABOUT THE WAR.

YOU WERE ASKING ABOUT PETER.

I STILL REMEMBER THAT SOUND. THE SOUND THAT REALLY WAS NO SOUND AT ALL.

WHEN MY EARS WORKED AGAIN I COULD HEAR WAR. IT WAS EVERYWHERE.

AND THEN HE APPEARED FROM NOWHERE. LIKE HE HAD BEEN THERE ALL ALONG, JUST...MY EYES HAD FAILED TO SEE HIM.

NEXT
FLOOR,
MOVE!

KABOOM

WHAT NOW? WE'RE TRAPPED!

SECOND WINDOW TO THE RIGHT.

ARE YOU CRAZY? THE GAP IS TWENTY FEET ACROSS! HOW ARE WE GOING TO MAKE THAT?

MAGIC?

WE WAIT HERE, WE GET PULVERIZED BY THE NEXT SHELL. I'M NOT ABOUT TO LET THAT HAPPEN.

SO, WHAT
DID HAPPEN?

THE IMPOSSIBLE.

HE BACKED UP,
READIED HIMSELF...

...GOT A FULL
HEAD OF STEAM...
AND BY GOD...

...PETER
FLEW.

OLD STORE ACROSS THE WAY. I'VE BEEN BUNKIN' THERE FOR WEEKS, PLACE IS ABANDONED. WE CAN HIDE OUT THERE TILL THE GERMANS ARE PUSHED OUTTA CALAIS.

AND IF THEY STAY?

ONE THING AT A TIME.

GO, GO.

JUST A LITTLE FURTHER. NICE, QUIET PLACE UPSTAIRS. C'MON.

I'M LOOKIN' FOR SOMEONE.

LOOKIN' MY WHOLE LIFE.

FOR WHO?

BELLE.

SHE'S BEEN REAL HARD TO FIND, BUT I FOLLOWED HER TO THIS TOWN. ROTTEN GERMANS MESSED IT ALL UP.

ENOUGH ABOUT ME, WHO ARE YOU?

FELIX.

JULIEN.

ALAIN.

CLAUDE.

MAURICE.

I'M GILBERT.

THANKS FOR SAVING OUR SKINS BACK THERE.

I'D HOPE ANY OF YOU'D DO THE SAME FOR ME.

RATA TAT TAT TAT TAT

BLOODY HELL.

CHRIST ALMIGHTY.

<ONE LESS BRIT TO WORRY ABOUT.>

GET BACK HERE!

WAIT, JUST... I--

BLAM

WUNDERBAR!

CHAPTER TWO

ISSUE TWO COVER B

ANY IDEA WHY HE DID THE WOLF CRY?

HAH, HE WAS A BIT OF A BRAGGART, I'M AFRAID. IT BECAME A SORT OF SYMBOL LATER, A CALLING CARD TO LET THE NAZIS KNOW WE WERE COMING.

HOW DID HIS ACTIONS MAKE YOU FEEL?

ALIVE.

... SCARED, BUT SO ALIVE.

I NEVER FELT TRULY SAFE WITH HIM. HE WAS AN ERRATIC YOUNG MAN. I...

HMM.

HAVE YOU EVER BEEN CHASED BY A DOG?

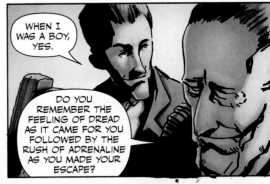

WHEN I WAS A BOY, YES.

DO YOU REMEMBER THE FEELING OF DREAD AS IT CAME FOR YOU FOLLOWED BY THE RUSH OF ADRENALINE AS YOU MADE YOUR ESCAPE?

HAH! I DO, ACTUALLY.

THAT IS WHAT BEING AROUND PETER WAS LIKE, MR. PARSONS...

"...LIKE BEING CHASED BY A WILD DOG."

AH AH AH! HANDS TO THE SKY, TROOPERS.

GET DOWN HERE!

ANYONE ELSE STARTING TO DOUBT WE'RE ANY SAFER WITH PETER THAN WE WERE IN THE COLLAPSING ORPHANAGE.

TAKE THEIR WEAPONS. ... CLOCK IS TICKING, BOYS.

THOUGHT YOU WERE RIGHT BEHIND ME, GILBERT.

I WAS... I'M JUST NOT...

NOT BRAVE LIKE YOU.

DON'T TOOTLE ALONG NEXT TIME, ALL RIGHT?

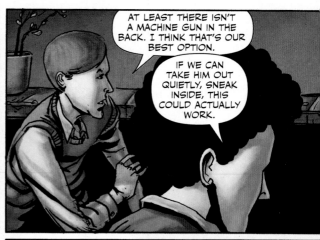

AT LEAST THERE ISN'T A MACHINE GUN IN THE BACK. I THINK THAT'S OUR BEST OPTION.

IF WE CAN TAKE HIM OUT QUIETLY, SNEAK INSIDE, THIS COULD ACTUALLY WORK.

ANY LUCK?

THERE'S A DOOR IN THE BACK ALLEY, BUT THEY'VE GOT A SOLDIER STATIONED THERE.

PRETTY SURE THERE'S ANOTHER ONE INSIDE AS WELL.

WHAT HAPPENS AFTER, WHEN WE FREE THE BRITS? I REALLY DOUBT WE'LL BE ABLE TO SNEAK ALL OF THEM OUT UNNOTICED.

WE HAVE TO BE VERY QUIET, THAT'S ALL.

I'M SAYING WE NEED TO HAVE A BACKUP PLAN.

I LIKE HOW YOU THINK, FELIX. IF THIS GOES BAD BUSINESS, RATHER SAFE THAN SORRY, RIGHT?

CAN I GET YOU ON THE ADJACENT ROOF, WATCH THE FRONT AND COVER US WITH YOUR SHOOTER IF WE NEED IT?

OH, I'LL HAVE YOU COVERED.

VROOOM

CLICK

THWUMP

‹SO I TOLD HIM, IF YOU WANT TO KNOW, COME LOOK FOR YOURSELF!›

HA HA HA HA!

WHAT THE HELL IS GOING ON DOWN THERE?

GIVE ME A BIT OF WARNING NEXT TIME. I'M ALL FOR BRASH PLANS, BUT WE NEED TO BE ON THE SAME PAGE.

UGHH, I THINK FELIX OVERDID THINGS. JUST *SLIGHTLY.*

NO MORE MACHINE GUN TO WORRY ABOUT. THAT'S WHAT'S IMPORTANT. GET THE BRITS BEFORE MORE GERMAN CHIENS TURN UP.

I WANTED TO HIT THEM BY SURPRISE.

OH, THEY WERE. YOU WANT TO MAKE SURE THAT YOUR TEAM ISN'T. GOOD WORK, THOUGH.

WE-WE KILLED HIM, PETER.

WE JUST REACTED.

NOT LIKE THEY DON'T DESERVE IT, ANYWAY.

PETE, I'VE FOUND THEM!

BUT WHAT WE WERE ABOUT TO WALK INTO WAS MUCH WORSE.

THINK WE'RE CLEAR, GO!

<FIRE!>

TAT TAT TAT. TAT TAT TAT

≥ECK≥

≥UGK≥

AHHHHHH!

I'M THE BEST THERE EVER WAS.

THWIP

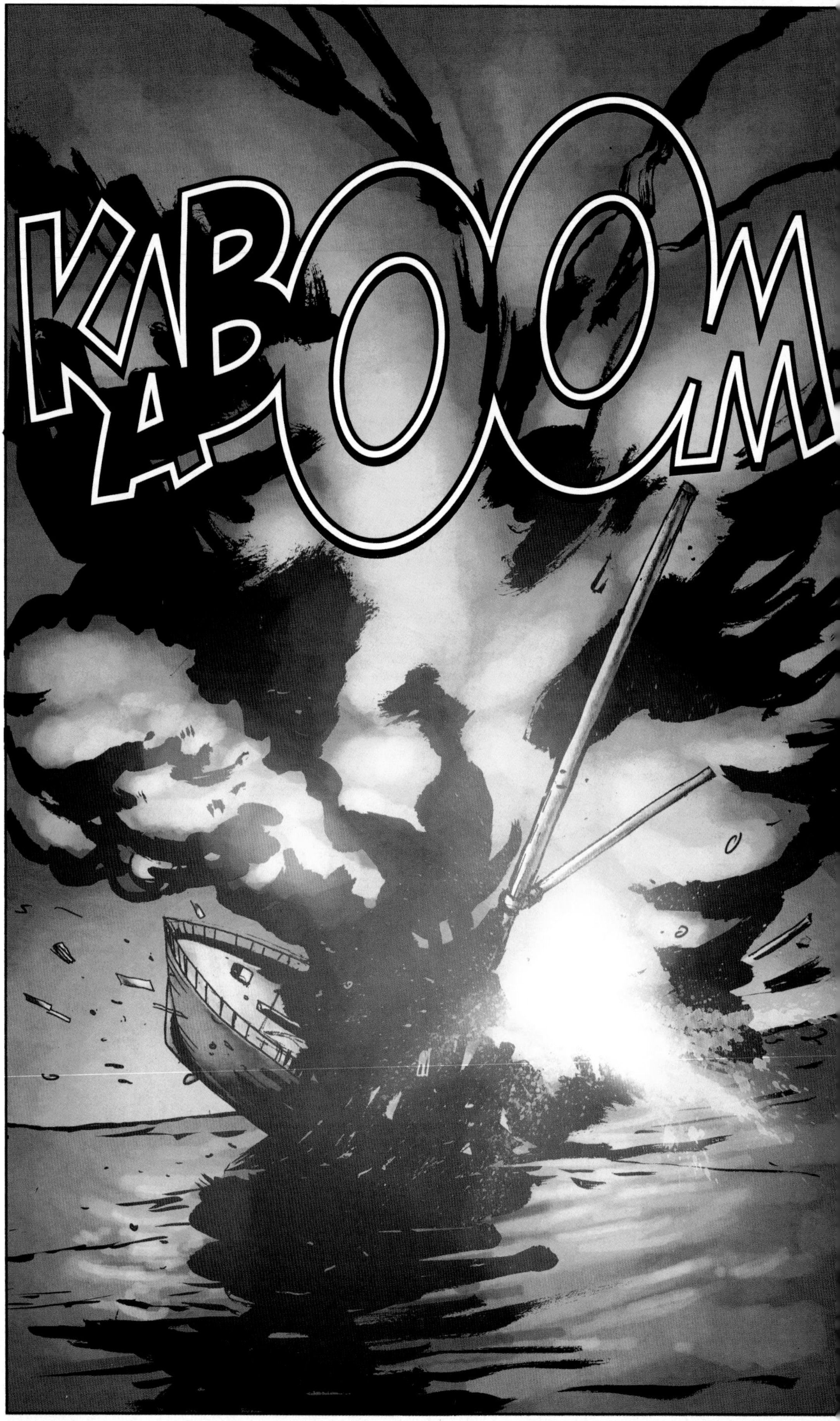
KABOOM

YOU WONDER ABOUT MANY THINGS WHEN IT SEEMS ALL HOPE IS LOST AND THAT PERHAPS YOUR TIME HAS COME TO AN END.

BUT YOU KNOW, THE FUNNY THING IS DESPITE EVERYTHING, ALL I COULD THINK OF WAS LITTLE LUCIEN BORDEAUX.

HE DIED IN THE ORPHANAGE BLAST AND YET, HERE I WAS, A DAY LATER SINKING TO THE BOTTOM OF THE OCEAN.

I WONDERED IF THE OTHER SIDE OFFERED PEACE, SOMETHING LUCIEN WAS ENJOYING WHILE THE REST OF US FOUGHT TO LIVE.

IT WAS THE FIGHT THAT KEPT ME ALIVE, MR. PARSONS.

BUT WHEN MY WILL TO SURVIVE FAILED...

THIS IS WHERE IT ALL HAPPENED. YOU KNOW, I HAVEN'T BEEN BACK TO THE HARBOUR SINCE THE EVACUATION.

THE MEMORY IS AS CLEAR AS EVER, THOUGH.

I'VE BEEN MEANING TO ASK...

YOU'VE MENTIONED A FEW RATHER STRENUOUS EXPERIENCES AND I'VE BEEN WONDERING HOW YOU WERE ABLE TO COPE AT SUCH A YOUNG AGE?

WHAT CHOICE DID I HAVE? IT WAS A TIME OF WAR, MR. PARSONS. MEN NOT MUCH OLDER THAN ME WERE GIVING THEIR LIVES TO DEFEND OUR COUNTRY, I WAS SIMPLY FIGHTING TO SEE ANOTHER DAY.

SOME OF US DIDN'T COPE SO WELL, BUT THAT'S WHY WE WERE INSEPARABLE. NOTHING COULD TEAR US APART BECAUSE WE HAD EXPERIENCED AMAZING AND TERRIFYING THINGS. TOGETHER.

WHEN I WAS SO YOUNG, I THOUGHT I'D NEVER GROW OLD. IN PETER'S COMPANY, TIME WORKED DIFFERENTLY SOMEHOW. YOU DIDN'T REALIZE THE PASSING OF DAYS.

I MISS OUR ADVENTURES. MORE THAN THAT...

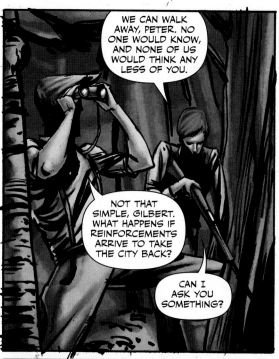

LET'S HOPE WE CAN GET ONE OF THESE RIGS GOING AS A DISTRACTION.

NO KEY.

WE'LL TRY THE NEXT ONE. GO 'ROUND BACK, STAY LOW.

NO KEYS.

‹GET DOWN ON THE GROUND! NOW!›

MERDE.

AHHH!

POW

‹CAREFUL, THERE'S TWO MORE!›

GUYS, ‹URGE A LITTLE HELP!

VERDAMMT!

VOILA!

EASY NOW, GENTLEMEN! EASE OFF THE SHOOTERS AND YOUR BUDDY HERE GETS TO ENJOY ANOTHER FRENCH SUNRISE.

YOUR CALL.

‹WHAT IS HAPPENING?›

‹KAPITÄN HAKEN, WE'VE BEEN...UM, AMBUSHED, SIR.›

‹CAUGHT US BY SURPRISE!›

‹WE ARE THE FORWARD SCOUTING POSITION, AND WE'VE BEEN CAUGHT BY SURPRISE?›

‹BAD FORM.›

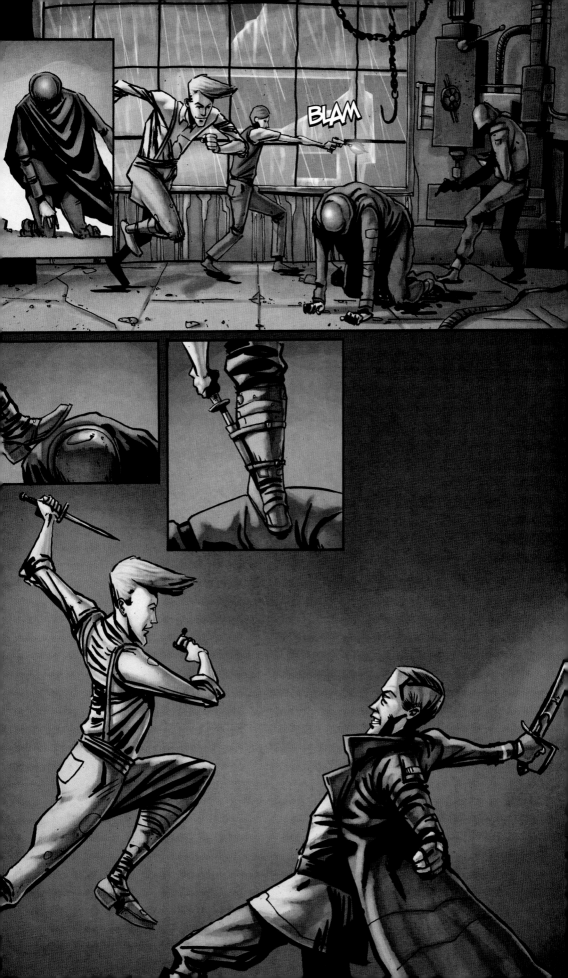

BLAM

HOPE YOU CAN FLY.

YOU'LL LIVE TO REGRET THIS DAY--

I DOUBT OUR PATHS WILL EVER CROSS AGAIN. AU REVOIR, KAPITAN!

THMUMP

THUNK

HUH, THOUGHT THE WINDOW WOULD BREAK.

WELL, I CAN'T BELIEVE WHAT I JUST SAW. CAN WE GO NOW, PLEASE?

BLAST THE RADIO. TAKE THE MACHINE GUN. WE'RE GETTING OUT OF HERE.

WHAT ABOUT HIM?

SAME AS THE REST, LEAVE HIM TO HIS FATE.

CHAPTER FOUR

A LOT OF TIME PASSED IN SILENCE AFTER THE DARLINGS JOINED US. AS ORPHANS, WE KNEW EXACTLY WHAT IT WAS THEY WERE GOING THROUGH, BUT TO FIND THE RIGHT WORDS...

WE WERE JUST BOYS.

FOR THE FIRST TIME SINCE OUR WAR STARTED WE WERE SAFE. THE OPEN ROAD AHEAD OF US AND THE BEAUTIFUL SPRING COUNTRYSIDE.

THAT WAS LIFE BACK THEN. ONE DAY AT A TIME.

WHERE WAS THIS PHOTOGRAPH TAKEN, GILBERT?

IN THE ORCHARD OF THE FARMHOUSE.

THE FARMHOUSE?

AH, YES. OUR HOME FOR A SHORT TIME. BY A STROKE OF LUCK WE FOUND THIS MAGICAL LITTLE PLACE TUCKED AWAY FROM THE REST OF THE WORLD.

HOW LONG AFTER YOUR ESCAPE FROM CALAIS?

NOT LONG. A FEW HOURS, AT MOST. WE WERE JUST HOPING FOR WATER BUT ENDED UP WITH SO MUCH MORE.

IT WAS IMPORTANT FOR WENDY, JOHN AND MICHAEL. THEY CARRIED SO MUCH HURT ON THEIR SHOULDERS, BUT AT THE FARM THEY FOUND TIME TO GRIEVE IN THE COMPANY OF PEOPLE WHO REALLY UNDERSTOOD.

WE ALL FOUND SOMETHING WE NEEDED THERE.

BUT... WE ALSO SUFFERED GREAT LOSS.

IT'S ALRIGHT, GILBERT. WE CAN MOVE ON IF YOU WANT.

THIS IS OUR STORY, MR. PARSONS. TO FULLY UNDERSTAND PARIS...

I'VE BEEN THINKING ALL DAY WHAT TO SAY TO THEM.

RIGHT WITH YOU ON THAT.

REALLY? PETER WITHOUT A PLAN?

GILBERT'S PUTTING TOGETHER SOME FOOD IF YOU'RE HUNGRY.

WE'RE FINE, THANK YOU.

I WANT SOMETHING TO EAT.

OUR LITTLE SECRET, MY FRIEND.

CAN YOU GET SOME GRUB? SANDWICHES OR SOMETHING?

I'LL TAKE A LOOK AROUND, TOO. SEE IF WE CAN'T SALVAGE ANY SUPPLIES BEFORE THE GERMANS SHOW UP.

YOU'RE A GOOD MAN, TOOTLES.

DON'T YOU GET STARTED ON THAT NOW.

WE MOVED TO CALAIS WHEN I WAS TEN. FATHER... ≈SIGH≈

FATHER OWNED AN ACCOUNTING FIRM IN LONDON BUT HAD PURCHASED A NEW OFFICE IN FRANCE. HE WANTED TO OVERSEE THE DEVELOPMENT PERSONALLY, AS WAS HIS WAY.

VERY MUCH A MAN OF DETAIL.

IT WAS ONLY MEANT TO BE A SHORT VISIT, BUT HE LOVED IT SO MUCH HERE.

I REMEMBER BEING SO SCARED LEAVING MY MATES BEHIND. MOTHER AND FATHER THREW A PART[Y] AND WE COULD INVITE WHOMEVER WE WANTE[D] WHILE THE PARENTS DRANK AND CHATTED DOWNSTAIRS, I WAS UPSTAIRS MAKING PROMISES TO JOANNA AND EMMA.

WHAT KIND OF PROMISES?

I NEVER WANTED TO GO TO CALAIS. I'D HAVE A ROW WITH FATHER ALMOST EVERY DAY LEADING UP TO THE MOVE.

"I'LL NEVER NEVER GO THERE!"

IT BECAME A LITTLE INSIDE JOKE BETWEEN ME AND MY MATES. I WAS MOVING TO NEVERLAND. WE MADE A VOW THE NIGHT OF THE PARTY THAT AS LONG AS WE WERE APART, WE WOULD STAY THE SAME. WE WOULD REFUSE TO AGE, AS THOUGH THAT WAS AN OPTION.

AS I SAID, ONE YEAR BECAME MANY MORE. I HAD NO CHOICE BUT TO GROW UP WITHOUT THEM, CARRY ON IN A WORLD WHERE I HAD NO SAY.

SO, I'M CURIOUS, HOW IS IT THAT YOU KNOW ABOUT PETER AND WENDY IN THE ORCHARD?

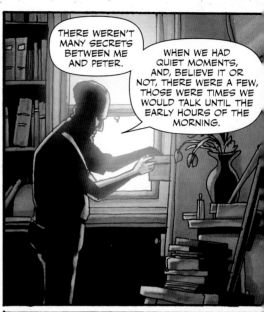

THERE WEREN'T MANY SECRETS BETWEEN ME AND PETER.

WHEN WE HAD QUIET MOMENTS, AND, BELIEVE IT OR NOT, THERE WERE A FEW, THOSE WERE TIMES WE WOULD TALK UNTIL THE EARLY HOURS OF THE MORNING.

ALL THIS TALK ABOUT THE FARM REMINDS ME OF A PHOTOGRAPH WENDY TOOK OF US. I THINK YOU'LL ENJOY IT.

SHE HAD A REAL TALENT FOR CAPTURING A MOMENT. I WAS ALWAYS ENVIOUS OF THAT.

WE'VE BEEN DISCUSSING THE POSSIBILITY OF STAYING HERE. WITH HOW DANGEROUS IT WAS JUST ESCAPING CALAIS, IT FEELS FOOLISH TO TEMPT FATE ANY MORE THAN WE ALREADY HAVE.

WE'RE ALL WITH JULIEN ON THIS.

WHAT ABOUT THE GERMANS? FOR ALL WE KNOW THEY'RE RIGHT BEHIND US.

I MENTIONED THAT, TOO. BUT, I THINK--

--THAT IT SHOULDN'T BE A PROBLEM. WE'RE IN THE MIDDLE OF NOWHERE.

FIRST OF ALL, THEY WILL NEVER TAKE ALL OF FRANCE AND EVEN IF THEY DID, WHAT INTEREST ARE THEY GOING TO HAVE IN THIS PLACE? I THINK--

--THE ENTIRE WAR COULD PASS US BY AND THIS COULD BE OUR HOME. SAFE. QUIET.

IT SEEMS LIKE A PRETTY BIG RISK. I STILL FEEL PARIS IS THE RIGHT CHOICE.

PETER, WHAT ARE YOU THINKING?

THE MAJORITY HAS SPOKEN. THIS IS OUR NEW HOME.

I'LL BE WITH HIM.

JOHN, I'D PREFER IF YOU STAYED HERE WITH US.

FELIX SAID HE'D SHOW ME HOW TO USE A RIFLE. I WANT TO BE PART OF THIS, WENDY. I DON'T WANT TO JUST SIT BACK AND LET THINGS HAPPEN.

LIKE FATHER DID.

I THINK WE SHOULD HIDE THE TRUCK IN THE BARN, JUST TO BE SAFE.

I'LL BE THERE IF YOU NEED ME.

I'M DONE WITH THAT LIFE.

JOHN... ≈SIGH≈

DON'T WORRY, HE'S IN GOOD HANDS. FELIX IS A BIT FOLLE DANS LA TÊTE, BUT HE'LL WATCH OVER JOHN.

WE'VE DIVIDED THE HOUSE UP FOR THE NIGHT. I'LL SHOW YOU WHERE YOU AND MICHAEL ARE SLEEPING.

AND SO WE STAYED.

EVEN THOUGH I ARGUED FOR PARIS, I WAS HAPPY TO STAY.

WE ALL WERE.

I'VE OFTEN THOUGHT ABOUT THOSE DAYS WE SPENT AT THE FARMHOUSE.

WHAT THEY REALLY MEANT TO ME. WHAT THEY MEANT TO EVERYONE WHO SHARED THEM.

THEY WERE VERY HAPPY TIMES.

THAT IS HOW I TRY TO REMEMBER IT...

...DESPITE WHAT COMES BACK TO ME IN MY DREAMS.

whirrrrrrrrr

WH!RRRRRRR

MERDE!

INCENDIER!

BESCHUSS!

AHHHH!

WE HAVE TO GET THE HELL OUT OF HERE! NOW!

WHAT'S GOING ON?

FRENCH ARMY AND GERMAN ARMY ARE HAVING IT OUT RIGHT HERE, RIGHT NOW!

WE GOTTA GET TO THE FRENCH SIDE!

BOOM

⟨CIVILIANS! WATCH YOUR FIRE!⟩

ALMOST THERE, C'MON!

WAIT!

WHERE'S ALAIN?

CHAPTER FIVE

WE CAME BACK TO CALAIS AFTER IT WAS LIBERATED BY THE ALLIES. THE FIRST THING WE DID WAS SCROUNGE WHAT LITTLE WE HAD TO PURCHASE A GRAVESTONE TO REMEMBER OUR FRIEND.

JUST ME WHO COMES BACK TO VISIT THESE LAST FEW YEARS. HARD FOR THE REST OF THEM TO MAKE IT.

GETS THAT WAY WHEN YOU'RE OLD, I'M AFRAID.

AH, YOU'RE STILL A YOUNG MAN YET, MR. AGNEW. THE WORLD'S YOUR OYSTER.

THANK YOU FOR HUMOURING AN OLD MAN HIS MEMORIES, MR. PARSONS.

NON, MERCI MR. AGNEW.

WE'D PLANNED A SMALL SURPRISE FOR ALAIN THE NIGHT HE DIED. I WAS NEVER ABLE TO GIVE HIM THE GIFT JULIEN AND I MADE TOGETHER.

I'VE HELD ON TO IT ALL THESE YEARS.

JULIEN WAS A FANTASTIC ARTIST. ALL OF MY CHILDREN, SO MANY TALENTS.

I'VE OFTEN WONDERED WHAT ALAIN WOULD'VE DONE WITH HIS LIFE.

HE TURNED FIFTEEN THE DAY HE DIED.

BON ANNIVERSAIRE, ALAIN.

HAPP[...]

BIRTHDAY!

A FRENCH OFFICER TOLD US TO FIND THE HIGHWAY, THAT WE'D FIND SOMEONE TO TAKE US AWAY FROM THE BATTLE.

WE RAN UNTIL MORNING.

I WAS LEAVING AN ENTIRE LIFE BEHIND ME, BUT PETER...

ALWAYS FACE FORWARD TO THE HORIZON.

FOR THAT MOMENT, I NEEDED ESCAPE.

TO FIND MY WAY TO A PLACE OUTSIDE OF TIME.

AND THERE IT WAS--

MERCI, MONSIEUR.

HE SAYS HE WAS HAPP TO HELP.

⟨YOU'RE MOST WELCOME. I HOPE YOU FIND YOUR WAY IN PARIS.⟩

PETE, THERE IS NO WAY THEY'LL LET US STAY HERE.

WE'VE ALL BEEN THROUGH A LOT. A GOOD SLEEP AND A TASTY MEAL WILL HELP. I WANT ALL OF YOU TO HAVE A NIGHT AWAY FROM...

WHAT HAPPENED.

HOW CAN WE AFFORD IT?

DON'T YOU WORRY ABOUT THAT.

FOUR ROOMS FOR THE NIGHT, GOOD SIR!

I'M AFRAID I CAN'T ALLOW YOU TO STAY WITHOUT PARENTS, BOY.

HOTEL POLICY, I AFRAID.

CRASH

27

AHHHH!

≶HUFF≶
≶HUFF≶

IT'S IN HERE SOMEWHERE...

AH, HERE WE GO!

WHO'S THIS?

THAT'S MY FATHER. HE DIED SIX MONTHS AGO.

I'M SORRY, PETE.

IT'S FINE, YOU KNOW WHAT THEY SAY. TIME HEALS ALL WOUNDS.

HE WAS A RICH MAN, CAME BACK WITH ALL KINDS OF IDEAS ABOUT INDUSTRY AFTER THE WAR. I WAS HIS ONLY CHILD.

MY MOTHER LEFT US WHEN I WAS A BABY. MISSED HOME TOO MUCH, THAT'S WHAT POPS SAID ANYWAY.

I CAME TO FRANCE TO SEE WHAT THE FUSS WAS ABOUT.

HEY, PETE! WE'RE GONNA GET SOME LOLLIES. YOU WANNA COME?

HE WON'T TAKE NO FOR AN ANSWER, I'M AFRAID.

HAHA, SURE THING, KID!

YOU COMIN'?

THAT WAS THE MOST HE EVER SAID ABOUT HIS FATHER.

SOON MAY BECAME JUNE AND THE WHOLE WORLD BEGAN TO CHANGE.

WE DID OUR BEST TO PRETEND OTHERWISE.

THERE'S...
SO MANY.

OH MY
GOD!

PETE! GILBERT!

WEITERGEHEN!

FELIX MADE IT?

PETER WAS RIGHT. FELIX WAS A FIGHTER. I SHOULD NEVER HAVE DOUBTED HIS ABILITY TO SURVIVE.

SO, DID YOU EVER SEE FELIX AGAIN?

AHHHH, BUT THAT IS NOT MY STORY TO TELL MR. PARSONS. WHAT CAME NEXT WAS AN ADVENTURE THAT CURLY SET IN MOTION.

YOU SEE, IT WAS ALL *HIS* IDEA.

THAT'S WHAT PETER CALLED JULIEN, CORRECT?

OUI.

I SUPPOSE THE ANSWER WAS OBVIOUS AFTER ALL THE PICTURES I'VE SEEN OF HIM.

THANK YOU FOR ALL OF THIS, MR. AGNEW. I KNOW IT WASN'T EASY AT TIMES.

DON'T BE SILLY, IT WAS AN HONOUR TO SHARE MY MEMORIES WITH YOU.

I HOPE YOU FIND WHAT YOU'RE LOOKING FOR, MR. PARSONS.

CALL ME JOHN.

OF COURSE, JOHN.

OH! I ALMOST FORGOT TO ASK...

...WHAT IS YOUR LAST MEMORY OF PETER?

PETER WAS MY BEST FRIEND. HE LIVES IN MY HEART AND MEMORIES, AND MY SPIRIT SWELLS WHEN I FIND MY WAY BACK TO THOSE MAGICAL TIMES.

NOTHING WAS EVER QUIET OR SIMPLE WITH THAT BOY, AS I'M SURE YOU'RE BEGINNING TO UNDERSTAND.

THERE IS A STORY YET TO BE TOLD, SOMETHING THAT HAPPENED MANY YEARS LATER.

IT IS A STORY YOU WILL HEAR IN YOUR SEARCH FOR ANSWERS.

IT WAS AFTER THIS THAT PETER SAID HE'D BE BACK, THAT HE'D ONE LAST THING TO DO.

HE DISAPPEARED INTO THE SUNSET AND WE NEVER SAW HIM AGAIN.

FOR YEARS I WONDERED WHY HE NEVER RETURNED. BUT YOU KNOW WHAT, JOHN?

IT MAKES PERFECT SENSE TO ME NOW...

EXTRAS

Teasers
Rejected cover
Sketchbook

RIGHT:
We've been producing teasers for new books for a couple of years now. These images go over the internet in the hope of enticing readers to try out a new series.

This image is a slightly altered version of the cover for issue number one.

Once they were LOST BOYS...
NOW they're Europe's best hope!

LEFT:
This teaser used the cover art for issue number two and, except for the copy, remained pretty much unchanged for both uses.

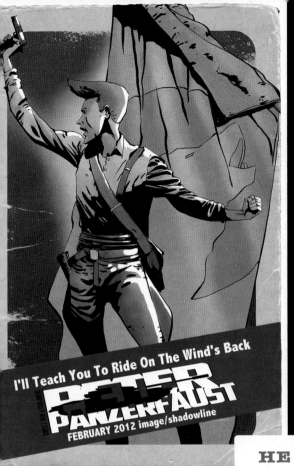

LEFT:
In a reversal of the previous two teasers, this image started as an original teaser and became the cover for the second printing of issue number two!
It was inspired by a World War Two poster.

RIGHT:
We all loved this page from issue number one so much that it not only was repurposed as a teaser image, but also served as the illustration for the inside front cover of the series and the credits page for this volume!

RIGHT:
Another teaser image that became a cover! In this case the illustration was used for the second printing of issue number one.

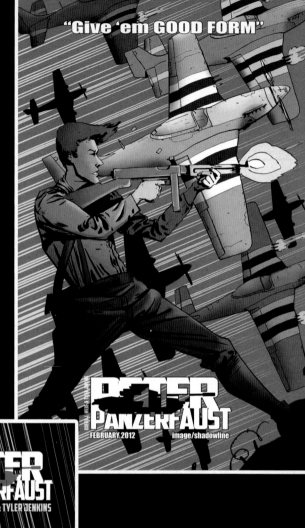

"Give 'em GOOD FORM"

PETER PANZERFAUST

FEBRUARY 2012   image/shadowline

PETER PANZERFAUST

KURTIS WIEBE & TYLER JENKINS

"TO DIE WOULD BE AN AWFULLY BIG ADVENTURE."

image   Shadowline

FEBRUARY 2012

LEFT:
And we close with a teaser image that that has never seen print before! This was the very first appearance of upcoming villain...Hook! A teaser, indeed.

This was the original cover for issue number four. Inspired by a World War Two era poster, Tyler Jenkins worked his tail off to try and get it right, but was never satisfied with the results. He felt he could do a better cover...and he was right! See page 77 for the beautiful cover he came up with on his own.

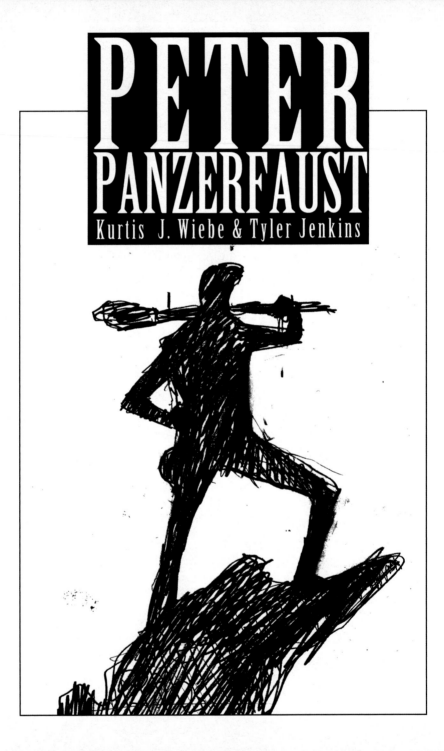

This was the very first sketch Tyler did of Peter Panzerfaust. Though rough, you can see the bravado Peter displays throughout the series in his defiant gesture. Just as a writer has to make copious notes about his plot, characters and pacing, so too does the artist draw uncountable sketches in an attempt to capture gesture, design and composition. Over the next few pages we'll give you a taste of how it's done.

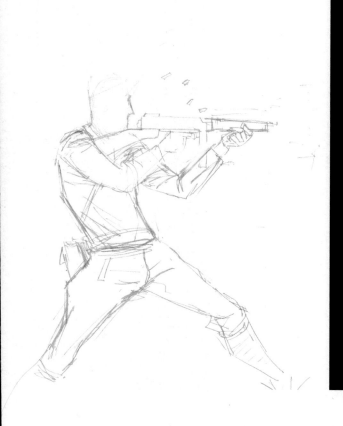

Two studies for the second printing cover of issue one (sans all of the Mustangs).

The one below made it to the final cover.

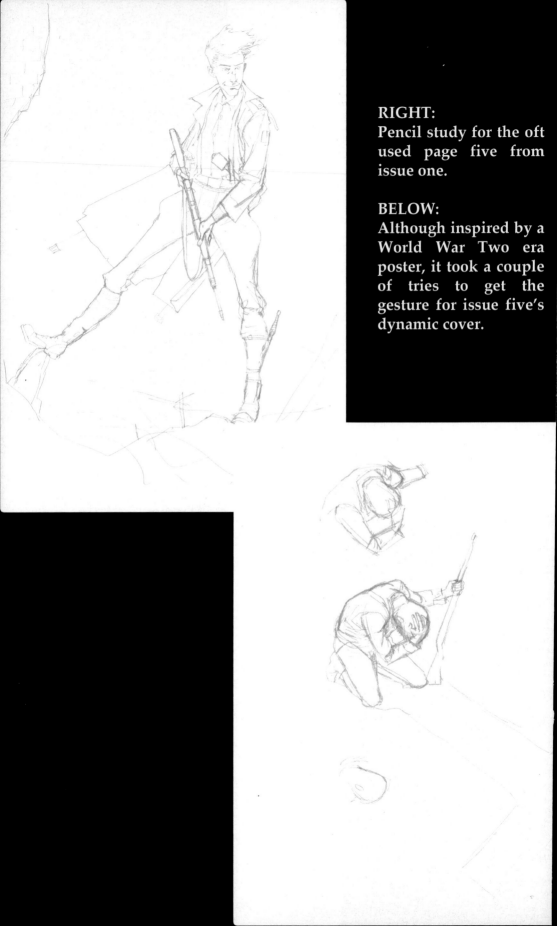

RIGHT:
Pencil study for the oft used page five from issue one.

BELOW:
Although inspired by a World War Two era poster, it took a couple of tries to get the gesture for issue five's dynamic cover.

Kurtis scoured the internet for World War Two era posters, some of which provided the inspiration for covers, others just didn't work out.

On these next two pages, we're going to show you some of the sketches alongside the posters that inspired them.

All of these sketches were done for issue four.

The piece above made it all the way to being colored before artist Tyler Jenkins felt it just wasn't good enough for a cover and rejected it.

The piece below never made it past the sketch stage.

RIGHT:
Tyler's pencil sketch for this volume's cover.

BELOW RIGHT:
The poster that inspired issue five's dynamic cover.

BELOW RIGHT:
We just thought it would be a fun way to close out this section and this volume.
Until next time, keep 'em flying.

KURTIS J. WIEBE

is a Vancouver, Canada based author who's been established in the world of comic writing since 2009. For his contribution to the critically acclaimed Green Wake, Kurtis was presented with the Outstanding Comic Book Writer Shuster Award. His other credits include Rat Queens, Peter Panzerfaust, Debris, Grim Leaper and Intrepids.

TYLER JENKINS

is a Canadian artist and comic creator, partially responsible for the nearly unknown Snow Angel and the surprisingly popular Peter Panzerfaust from Image Shadowline. He lives on a farm in the middle of somewhere with his wife and 2 kids. He hopes to never retire anywhere.